Puzzle Compilation: Jenny Lynch
Design: Theodore Szpindel
Editors: Amy Brem-Wilson and Simon Melhuish

Published by:
LAGOON BOOKS

ISBN 1-90281-375-8
© 2016 LAGOON BOOKS
Lagoon Books is a trademark of Lagoon Trading Company Limited. All rights reserved. Reprinted 2016.

Printed in China.

mindbending CLASSIC LOGIC PUZZLES

ALL THE MINDBENDING
PUZZLE BOOKS HAVE BEEN
CAREFULLY COMPILED TO GIVE
THE READER A REFRESHINGLY
WIDE RANGE OF CHALLENGES,
SOME REQUIRING ONLY A
SMALL LEAP OF PERCEPTION,
OTHERS DEEP AND DETAILED
THOUGHT. ALL THE BOOKS
SHARE AN EYE-CATCHING AND
DISTINCTIVE VISUAL STYLE THAT
PRESENTS EACH PROBLEM IN AN
APPEALING AND INTRIGUING
WAY. DO NOT, HOWEVER, BE
DECEIVED; WHAT IS EASY ON
THE EYE IS NOT NECESSARILY
EASY ON THE MIND!

Aunt Tabitha was extremely touchy about her age. When an impudent nephew was brave enough to ask her, she cunningly replied that she was 35 years old, not counting Saturdays or Sundays. How old was she?

Three brothers entered a shop, each needing a pair of shoes resoled and a key cut. There are two assistants in the shop, both of whom work at the same speed. It takes 15 minutes to resole a pair of shoes and 5 minutes to cut a key. How quickly can they finish?

A man died leaving nearly £8000 to be divided between his widow, four daughters and three sons. He stipulated that each daughter should receive twice as much as their mother and each son receive twice as much as their mother. If the exact amount left was £7936, how much should the widow receive?

Using all the numbers from 1 to 25, fill in the grid below so that all rows, columns and diagonals add up to 65. The first number has been placed for you.

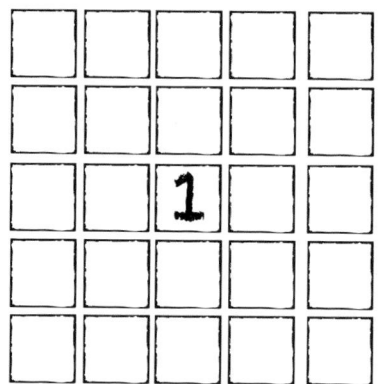

Can you write down a straightforward subtraction sum, a – b = c, where each of the numbers (a, b and c) are made up of nine digits, 1-9 inclusive, with each digit being used once only in each number?

A couple who have been married 65 years were both born on August 16th, seven years apart. The man is 2555 days older than his wife. In what years were they born?

Imagine that the three grids can be placed on top of each other to form a three dimensional cube. Put the given numbers onto the grids so that each line, down, across and through, will add up to 12. You do not have to bother with diagonals.

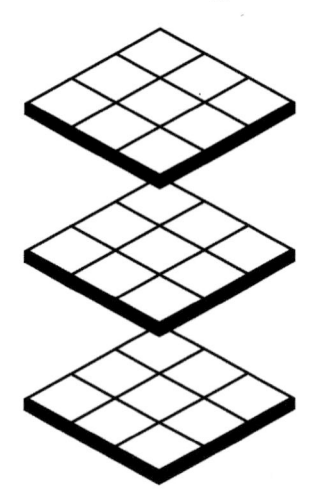

1 1 2 2 2 2 3 3 3 3 3 3 4 4 4 4 4 5 5 5 5 6 6 6 7 7 8

Insert plus and minus signs to achieve the totals given:

12   3   4   5   6   =   10

2   2   3   4   5   =   0

7   6   2   5   1   =   7

5   4   3   1   4   =   9

8   4   5   2   1   =   8

It takes a motor boat 2 minutes to travel 2km when going with the current and 4 minutes when going against the current. The current is always constant. How long would it take the boat to do the same journey in slack water, when there is no current at all?

Two fences need to be whitewashed. One is half the area of the other. A group of workmen spend half a day working on the large fence before splitting into two equally sized smaller groups, one of whom start work on the smaller fence. At the end of the day, the large fence had been done but there still remains a metre of the smaller fence to do. One of the lads from the second group returns the next day and it takes him all day to finish the job. If all the lads work at the same pace – how many lads are in the original group?

8 grapefruits, 7 oranges and 3 lemons weigh the same as 3 oranges, 6 grapefruits and 6 lemons. If a grapefruit weighs 2/3 as much as a lemon and if a dozen oranges weigh 3 kilos, how much does a lemon weigh?

Can you arrange the coins so that coins with adjacent values are never in adjacent boxes? (e.g. the 20p must not be in the same row or column as the 10p or 50p).

Even though they reduced the fares, so that no fare was over £1, there were never more than 40 passengers on any one vehicle run by the Weston-Super-Mare bus company. One day, everyone that got on the bus paid exactly the same fare in exactly the same 7 coins. When he reached the terminus, the driver had collected £13.35 in fares. If I tell you that he did not have a single 20p piece, can you determine how many 2p coins he had?

A truck driver picked up a hitchhiker as he travelled northwards out of the city. After some time, the hitchhiker remarked that every 10 minutes they passed a truck going in the opposite direction. "How many trucks will arrive in the city in an hour?" he asked, "assuming that the trucks are travelling at equal speeds in both directions?" The driver replied "Six. It's obvious because 60 divided by 10 is 6." Was he correct?

If a clock takes 2 seconds to strike 2 o'clock, how long will it take to strike 3 o'clock?

Use the numbers to complete the magic square so that all the columns and rows add up to 30.

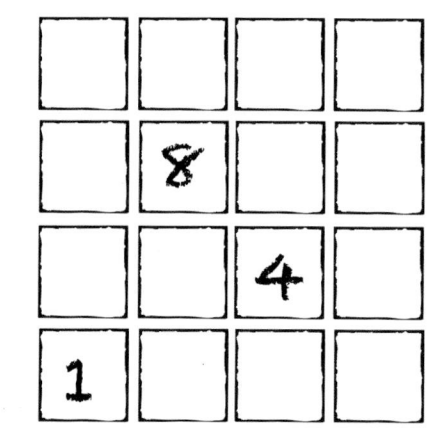

1 2 3 4 5 6 10 11 12 12 13 14 14

Use the following
mathematical signs so that
? = 4. There are two possible
solutions. Use the same signs
so that ? = 2. How many
solutions can you find?

2   2   2   2   2   2   = ?

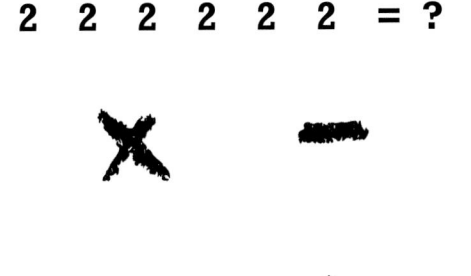

How old would a person born in 50 BC be on their birthday in 50 AD?

If a man walks due south for 4 miles and then due north for 3 miles, what is the maximum distance he can be from where he started?

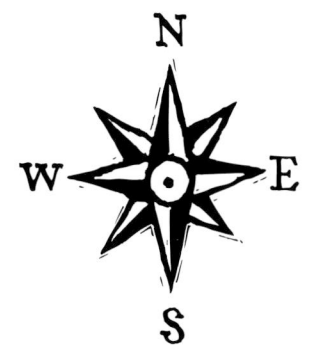

Bill and Ben's combined age is 91. Bill is now twice as old as Ben was when Bill was as old as Ben is now. How old are they?

Find the next number
in each series and
explain how the series
is constructed.

4 6 26 666 ?

22 20 10 8 4 2 ?

2 4 13 26 35 70 ?

$5^1/_5$ $4^1/_4$ $3^1/_3$ $2^1/_2$?

3 4 5 7 9 13 15 19 21 ?

If a man spends one fifth of what is in his wallet and then one fifth of what remains and has spent a total of £72.00, what was the amount originally in his wallet?

Divide 470 marbles between three boys so that Andrew gets 120 more than Bill, who receives 70 more than Colin. How many does each boy receive?

There is a pack of cards numbered 1-60. If these cards are thoroughly shuffled, and all cards are dealt. What is the likelihood that cards 1, 2, 3 and 4 will appear in ascending numerical order somewhere in the display?

Put the numbers in the magic square so that all columns, rows and diagonals add up to 38:

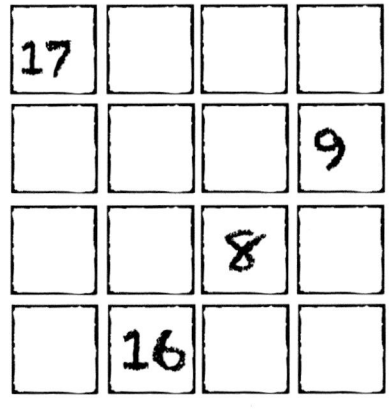

17			
			9
		8	
	16		

6 10 5 7 11 4 3 12 2 13 15 14

Sally bought a bracelet for £21 which she then resold for £25. She unwisely accepted a cheque from the purchaser for £35 and gave them £10 change. She then gave the cheque to her landlord but it bounced. She had to borrow a further £35 to pay the rent. How much money has Sally actually lost?

Sam won the lottery! He spent 95p the first day, £1.90 the next, £2.85 the next, £3.80 the next and so on. Each day he spent 95p more than the day before, until he finally spent the last £190 of his winnings. How much did he win in total?

If I save 1p on the first day of the month, 2p on the second, 4p on the third and continue, each day saving twice as much as the day before, how much will I have saved by the last day of January?

Susie could not sleep. One night she went to bed at 10.15 and read her book. Three quarters of an hour later she put out her light and eventually drifted off. Sometime later a noise awoke her. Gazing at her alarm clock, she noticed that the hands were exactly overlapping. A little over fifteen minutes later she fell asleep again before waking up to see that the digits on the radio alarm were all the same. She dozed fitfully over the next four and a half hours before getting up for breakfast. What time was it when she got up?

Madge, Muriel and Mandy were playing poker. During the first round, Madge won as much from Muriel as Madge had had originally. In the second hand, Muriel won as much from Mandy as she had left. After the third hand, Mandy won from Madge as much as Mandy then had left. At the end of the game, they each had £40. How much did each player have at the start of the game?

What is the next number in each series:

1 9 1 4 1 9 1 8 1 9 3 9 1 9 4 ?

166.66666 187.5 214.28571 250 300 ?

10 15 13 18 16 21 19 24 22 ?

940 839 738 637 ?

4 8 32 512 131072 ?

Sylvester left £650 to be divided amongst his five grandchildren, all of whom were different ages. The money was to be divided in order of age, each child receiving £25 more than the next child younger to them. How much did the youngest child receive?

Gentleman A has £200 and Gentleman B £96. Take money from both so that you take twice as much from A as from B and leave three times as much to A as you do to B. How much money should you take from each to satisfy the requirements?

A teapot and strainer cost £32. If the teapot costs £30 more than the strainer, what is the price of each?

Use each of the four digits
to make the target number.
Each digit must be used
once. Numbers may be
added, subtracted, divided or
multiplied and digits can be
combined in pairs or threes.

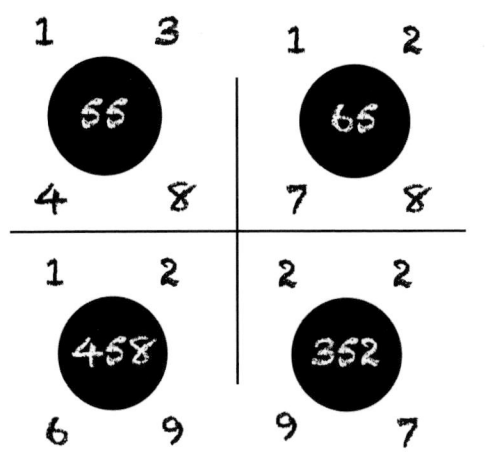

At any gathering where more than two people are present, there will be at least two people who have exactly the same number of friends present. Is this true or false?

A woman has three daughters who in turn, each have three daughters. If they all get together in one room:

1. How many pairs of sisters are present?

2. How many pairs of mothers and daughters are there?

3. How many pairs of aunts and nieces are there?

4. How many pairs of cousins are there?

5. How many pairs of grandmothers and granddaughters are there?

6. How many people are there in the room?

Three friends shared out 24 liquorice allsorts, each getting a number according to what their age had been three years previously. The youngest then proposed he would halve his share, keep one half and divide the other half amongst the other two friends. But in order for him to do this, the middle friend should promise to do the same, followed by the eldest. When they had done this, each person was left with 8 liquorice allsorts. What are the ages of the friends?

Can you:

> Use four 4s to make 44
> Use five 5s to make 55
> Use six 6s to make 66
> Use seven 7s to make 77
> Use eight 8s to make 88

You can group the digits in pairs or threes and numbers can be added, subtracted or multiplied.

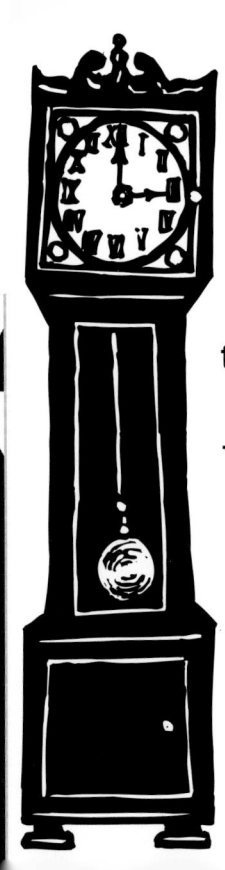

There are two clocks; one of which goes one minute per hour too slow and the other goes thirty seconds per hour too fast. If I wind them up and start them at the same time, how long would it be before one clock was exactly one hour ahead of the other?

A train takes 2 seconds to enter a tunnel which is 2km long. If the train is travelling at 180km per hour, how long will it take to pass completely through the tunnel?

If four knitters can knit four stitches in four seconds, how many stitches can twelve knitters knit in twelve seconds?

When I was 14, my mother was 41 and she is now twice as old as I am. How old am I?

A beggar collecting cigarette ends can make a new cigarette out of four ends. One morning he collects a total of thirty-two ends. How many cigarettes can he smoke that day?

Arrange these digits **1 2 3 4 5 6 7** to form a three digit multiple of four and a four digit multiple of three.

Arrange these digits **2 3 4 5 6 7 8** to form a three digit multiple of four and a four digit multiple of five.

Arrange these digits **1 2 3 4 5 6 7 8 9** to form a three digit multiple of three, a three digit multiple of four and a three digit multiple of five.

1234567

2345678

123456789

In a local hardware shop, 1 costs 14p yet it costs 28p for 50 and 42p for 144. What is being bought?

A general had twenty eight guards with which to safeguard a princess. He had eight lookout posts and so he arranged his troops as in the diagram, in order to ensure that each wall of the castle was guarded by nine men. At the end of the first day, four men were killed. How could he rearrange the remaining men to ensure that nine men would still guard each wall? At the end of the second day, a further four men were killed. Can he still ensure that each wall is guarded by nine men?

You can use all nine digits (1-9) in this calculation. The 4 has already been used, there are two possible solutions. What are they?

$$? ? ? ?$$
$$\times\ 4$$
$$\overline{? ? ? ?}$$

$$? ? ? ?$$
$$\times\ 4$$
$$\overline{? ? ? ?}$$

If six squirrels can eat 6 acorns in 1/10 of an hour, how many would it take to eat 100 acorns in 6000 seconds?

If a clock turned into a twenty four hour clock so that it struck 24 times at midnight, how many times would it strike in the course of a 24 hour day?

Jack made a bet with Jill. "I bet you one pound, that if you give me two pounds, I will give you three pounds in return." "Sounds good to me!" said Jill. But is it?

Use three identical digits in a simple addition sum so that the total is 12. You cannot use the digit 4.

How many squares are there in this diagram?

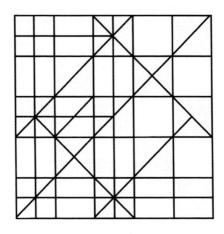

Beatrice ate 2/3 as many cakes as Annabel would have eaten if Annabel had eaten 6 more than half as many as Beatrice would have eaten if Beatrice had eaten 3 less than Annabel would have eaten. Just how many cakes did Beatrice eat?

If a man and a half can tarmac a road and a half in a day and a half, how many roads can 6 men tarmac in seven days?

Arrange the below digits to form four square numbers (there are 3 possible solutions). Now try three square numbers.

1 2 3 4 5 6 7 8 9

Asked about his children, a man replied, "they are all redheads but two, all brunettes but two and all blondes but two". How many children did he have?

If a pig weighs 30kg plus half its own weight, how much does it weigh?

Fred dozed off during a particularly dull business presentation. He woke with a start and stole a furtive glance at his watch, only to find that both the hands were at exactly the same position as they had been when the meeting had started. Yet the presentation appeared to be drawing to an end. What had happened? The meeting had started between 10 and 12am. What time was it now?

Fill in the circles with the numbers given, so that the four circles on any one straight line add up to 35.

15 14 13 11 10 9 8 7 6 5 4 3

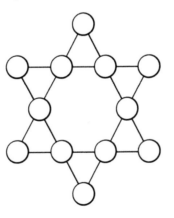

Eric's mum has given him a large Christmas cake. He knows from experience that if he eats a piece every day, it will take him 25 days to finish it. If he shares it with his friend, little Ernie and they both have a piece each day, it will only take 18 days to finish the cake. Eric and Ernie have the same size piece each day – but Eric's piece is not the same size as Ernie's. So, how long would it take Ernie on his own to devour the whole cake?

The ages of a certain father and son are the same with the digits reversed. Nine years ago, the father was twice as old as the son. How old are they now?

Divide 45 pencils amongst four friends, Rob, Bob, Bim and Tim, so that the following is possible: were you to give a further two to Rob, take two away from Bob, multiply what Bim had by two and divide what Tim has by two, all four friends would end up with the same number. How many do you need to give to each person initially?

What is the smallest possible value of a number that leaves a remainder of 1 when divided by 2, 3, 4, 5, or 6, but not when it is divided by 7?

In a certain family, each girl has as many sisters as brothers but each boy has twice as many sisters as brothers.
How many children are there?

A crate weighs three quarters of a crate plus three quarters of a pound. How heavy is it?

A man buys 10 trees. Can he plant the 10 trees in 5 rows with 4 trees in each row?

Fill in each circle so that the four circles on any one of the larger circles will add up to 30.

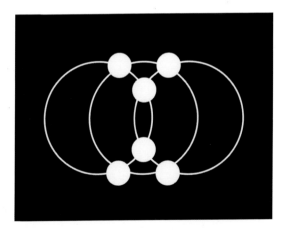

Professor Boffin has discovered an exciting mathematical phenomena concerning fractions with digits under 100. If he cancels identical digits above and below the line, the fraction is still correct. Can you find three fractions of which this is true?

Mary was meant to proofread a document at the rate of 30 pages a day. Lazy Mary was half way through the document before she realised that she was only working at the rate of 15 pages a day. How fast does she need to proofread the rest of the document in order to reach her target of 30 pages per day?

A mystery number with two identical digits is multiplied by 99. What is the four digit number which results, if the third digit of that number is 3?

Albert and Ida's ages are the same with the digits reversed. The difference between their ages is twice the age of Ed. Ida is ten times Ed's age. How old is everyone?

A forgetful gran was searching for presents for her two grandchildren. However, she couldn't remember what sex the children were. "I know they aren't both boys" she said. If this is true, what is the probability that they are both girls?

Mary needed 400ml of vegetable stock for a recipe she was following. However, the only measuring containers she had were 300ml and 500ml. How can she measure out exactly 400ml?

I bought 4 pencils at 2p each, 5 pens at 8p each, 8 notepads and 16 stamps. All items were individually priced, though I cannot remember the prices of the last two items, I can confidently query a bill of £2.10. Why is this?

Two horsemen started out at daybreak. They travelled the same distance and arrived at their destination at the same time. A rode twice as long as B rested and B rode for three times as long as A rested. Who rode the fastest?

Fill in this magic square so that all columns, rows and diagonals add up to 105.

A number with 4 at the end becomes 4 times larger when the number 4 is removed and put in front. What is the number?

Fill in the magic square so that all columns, rows and diagonals add up to 50. In addition, each group of four squares which make up another square inside the grid, needs to add up to 50 as well!

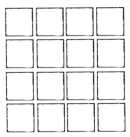

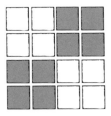

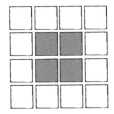

Use the numbers 0-15 to fill in the diagram, so that the numbers in each circle and on each straight line of four, add up to 30.

0 1 2 3 4 5 6 7 8 9 10 11 12 13 14 15

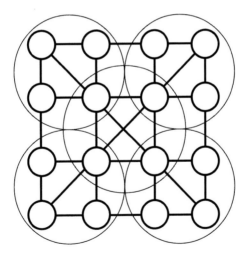

Ma Baker made some pizza dough using extra strong yeast. When left in a warm place it always doubles in size every 24 hours. If it takes 4 days to rise to the top of her extra large bowl, after how long would it be exactly half way up the bowl?

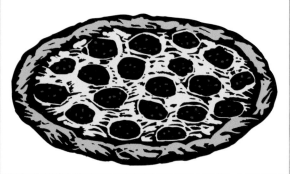

SOLUTIONS

solutions

p. 6   49

p. 7   30 minutes (one assistant does 1 pair of shoes and 3 keys, the other does 2 pairs of shoes)

p. 8   £256

p. 9   Here is one solution:

     9   11   18   5   22
     3   25   7   14   16
     12   19   1   23   10
     21   8   15   17   4
     20   2   24   6   13

p. 10   987654321
       − 123456789
       ——————
       864197532

p. 11   1896 and 1903.
2555 is an exact multiple of 365 so the intervening seven years did not include a leap year.
The two years must therefore be either side of a century end, in which case no leap year occurs.
(The next leap year after 1896 would be 1904.)

p. 12

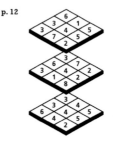

p. 13 $12 + 3 - 4 + 5 - 6 = 10$

     $2 + 2 - 3 + 4 - 5 = 0$

     $7 - 6 + 2 + 5 - 1 = 7$

     $5 + 4 - 3 - 1 + 4 = 9$

     $8 - 4 + 5 - 2 + 1 = 8$

p. 14   2 minutes, 40 seconds
The boat travels at 1/2 km per min when going against the current and 1 km per min when going with the current. So the current makes a 1/4 km difference and the boat speed must be 3/4 km per min. A 2 km journey travelling at 3/4 km per min would take 2 2/3 mins.

p. 15 Eight. The large fence took half a group day in the morning and a quarter in the afternoon ie. 3/4 group day. The smaller fence is half the area of the larger one so will take 3/8 of a group day, that makes 1 1/8 group days altogether. If there is 1/8 group day left to do and one man does it in one day, the group must total 8 men.

p. 16 600g

p. 17 20p   5p   £1
2p   50p   10p

p. 18 If there were never more than 40 passengers, then £13.35 could be made up by 15 people paying 89p or 5 people paying 267p or 3 people paying 445p. As no fare is over £1 we know that the first option is the correct one.
89p could be made up of seven coins in two different ways: either:

50 + 20 + 10 + 5 + 2 + 1 + 1
or 50 + 10 + 10 + 10 + 5 + 2 + 2

If the driver has no 20p pieces then the second option is how people actually paid. If each fare contained two 2p's, the total number he has is thirty.

p. 19 No. If the driver and hitchiker were stationary then he would be correct, but they are moving too. It takes them 10 minutes to meet a truck, but each time they pass one, it takes that truck a further 10 minutes to reach the point where they last met a truck. So the actual time between trucks is 20 minutes not 10. In fact, only three trucks arrive in the city every hour.

p. 20 4 seconds. If the time between the clapper striking the bell for the first peal and the second peal is 2 seconds, then it will be a further two seconds before it strikes for the third peal.

p. 21

12	3	1	14
6	8	12	4
11	5	4	10
1	14	13	2

solutions

p. 22 $2 - 2 \div 2 + 2 \times 2 = 4$
$2 \div 2 + 2 \times 2 - 2 = 4$

There are sixteen ways to achieve the total 2:

$2 + 2 \times 2 \div 2 - 2 = 2$
$2 - 2 + 2 \div 2 \times 2 = 2$
$2 + 2 \div 2 \times 2 - 2 = 2$
$2 - 2 + 2 \times 2 \div 2 = 2$
$2 + 2 - 2 \times 2 \div 2 = 2$
$2 - 2 \div 2 \times 2 + 2 = 2$
$2 + 2 - 2 \times 2 \div 2 = 2$
$2 - 2 \times 2 \div 2 + 2 = 2$
$2 \times 2 \div 2 - 2 + 2 = 2$
$2 + 2 - 2 \times 2 \div 2 = 2$
$2 \times 2 - 2 + 2 \div 2 = 2$
$2 + 2 - 2 \div 2 \times 2 = 2$
$2 \times 2 \div 2 + 2 - 2 = 2$
$2 + 2 \div 2 \times 2 - 2 = 2$
$2 \times 2 \div 2 + 2 - 2 = 2$
$2 + 2 \times 2 \div 2 - 2 = 2$

p. 23 99. There is no year 0.

p. 24 7 miles. It all depends on where on the globe his walk is taken.

If he starts four miles from the South pole and walks in a straight line towards it and then continues past it in a straight line, he is now

walking north and could continue a further three miles.

p. 25 Bill is 52, Ben is 39.

p. 26 **443546** – multiply the number by itself and minus 10
1 – minus 2 and divide by 2 alternately
79 – multiply by 2 and add 9 alternately
2 – ie. 1 1/1
25 – prime numbers with 2 added to each

p. 27 £200

p. 28 Andrew receives 260, Bill 140 and Colin 70.

p. 29 1 in 24! There are 24 ways 1 – 2 – 3 – 4 can fall, only one of which is in ascending order

p. 30 17 4 3 14
6 11 12 9
10 7 8 13
5 16 15 2

p. 31 £31. She has lost the £21 originally spent on the bracelet plus the £10 which she gave as change. She failed

to make the £4 profit she
hoped for but this cannot
count as money lost.

p. 32 £19,095

p. 33 £10,737,418.23

p. 34 8:03am

p. 35 Madge started with £30,
Muriel with £50 and Mandy
with £40

p. 36 **5** – the years of two
world wars
375 – 1500 divided by 9,
then 8, then 7, then six etc
27 – add 5 and minus 2
alternately
536 – subtract 101 each time
8589934592 – multiply
each number by half of itself

p. 37 £80

p. 38 Take £176 from **A** and £88
from **B**

p. 39 £31 and £1

p. 40 916 ÷ 2 = 458

$(7 + 9) \times 22 = 352$
$(4 + 3) \times 8 - 1 = 55$
$71 - (8-2) = 65$

p. 41 It is true.

If there are x number of
people at the party and you
were to label each person
with the number of friends
they had there, the numbers
could go from 0 to x−1.
However you cannot have
both 0 and x−1 because if
there is someone present who
has no friends (0), there
cannot be someone there
who knows everyone (x−1).
Therefore there are at most
x−1 labels for x number of
people and one of the labels
must appear twice.

p. 42 1. 12
2. 12
3. 18
4. 27
5. 9
6. 13

91

solutions

p. 43 7, 10 and 16

p. 44 The simplest methods are:

$$44 - (4 - 4) = 44$$

$$(5 \times 5) + (5 \times 5) + 5 = 55$$

$$66 - 66 + 66 = 66$$

$$(7 \times 7) + (7 \times 7) - 7 - 7 - 7 = 77$$

$$888 - 888 + 88 = 88$$

There are others!

p. 45 The faster clock gains on the slow one by the rate of one minute thirty seconds per hour. After 40 hours the faster clock will be exactly one hour ahead.

p. 46 Travelling at 180 km an hour, the train would take 20 seconds to travel 1 km and therefore 40 seconds to travel 2 km, plus 2 seconds for the complete train to pass any point, making a total of 42 seconds.

p. 47 36

p. 48 27 (as this is the difference in age between the two)

p. 49 Ten. He can make eight cigarettes, smoke them and make a further two cigarettes out of those eight ends.

p. 50 532 and 7641

632 and 8745

861, 932 and 745

p. 51 House numbers at 14p per digit

p. 52 After day one:

```
3 3 3
3     3
3 3 3
```

After day two:

```
4 1 4
1     1
4 1 4
```

p. 53
```
 1963    and    1738
  x4             x4
 ____           ____
 7852           6952
 ____           ____
```

p. 54 It would take six squirrels to eat 100 acorns in 6000 seconds (100 minutes)

p. 55 300

p. 56 Not from Jill's point of view!

If she gives him two pounds, Jack can renege on the deal and only needs hand over one pound, thereby making a one pound profit for himself.

had started at 10:59 and Fred awoke at 11:54.

p. 57 11+1 = 12

p. 58 76

p. 59 Six

p. 60 28

p. 61 You could have:

9 (3^2), 81 (9^2), 324 (18^2), and 576 (24^2)

OR 9, 25 (5^2), 361 (19^2), and 784 (28^2)

OR 1, 36 (6^2), 529 (23^2), and 784

To form 3 square nos: 25, 841 (29^2), and 7396 (86^2)

p. 62 3

p. 63 60 kg

p. 64 The hands had actually changed places. The meeting

p. 65

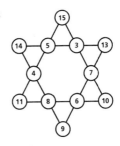

p. 66 64.28 days.
If Eric eats a cake in 25 days, he is eating 4% a day (100/25 = 4). Together they finish the cake in 18 days, so they eat it at the rate of 5.555a day (100/18 = 5.5550). Therefore Ernie must eat at the rate of 1.555% a day (5.555 – 4). 100/1.555=64.28.

p. 67 63 and 36

p. 68 Rob 8, Bob 12, Bim 5, Tim 20

p. 69 301

p. 70 Three boys and four girls

p. 71 3 pounds

p. 72

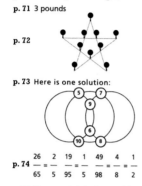

p. 73 Here is one solution:

5 7
9
6
10 8

p. 74 $\dfrac{26}{65} = \dfrac{2}{5}$ $\dfrac{19}{95} = \dfrac{1}{5}$ $\dfrac{49}{98} = \dfrac{4}{8} = \dfrac{1}{2}$

p. 75 She cannot do it. She would need to finish it in 0 days, i.e. now!

p. 76 6534 (99 x 66).

If you try all the possible numbers, a pattern emerges: 11 x 99 = 1089

22 x 99 = 2178

33 x 99 = 3267 etc.

The first and third digits always add up to 9, so the answer must be 6 —3 —. The second digit is always one

less than the first, so it must be 653 –. The second and fourth digits always add up to nine, so the answer is 6534.

p. 77 Ed is $4\frac{1}{2}$, Ida 45 and Albert 54

p. 78 If we know that they aren't both boys, then the probability of them both being girls is one in three.

p. 79 She should fill the 500 ml container first and use this to fill the 300ml container, thereby leaving 200 ml in the larger jug. Then she could empty the 300ml container back into the stock jar and pour the 200ml from the larger container into the 300ml container. If she once again fills the larger container from the jar and again, fills the smaller container from this, the smaller container needs 100ml to fill it, which will leave 400ml in the larger container.

p. 80 Everything is divisible by four but £2.10 is not, so it cannot be the correct total.

p. 81 If X = amount of time A rode and Y = amount of time B rode, then A rode X hours and rested Y, then B rode Y hours and rested X.

$$X + \frac{1}{3} Y = Y + \frac{1}{2} X$$

$$X = \frac{4}{3} Y$$

If A rode more to go the same distance, then B was going faster.

p. 82
25	32	9	16	23
31	13	15	22	24
12	14	21	28	30
18	20	27	29	11
19	26	33	10	17

p. 83 102564

p. 84
8	9	14	19
13	20	7	10
11	6	17	16
18	15	12	5

p. 85

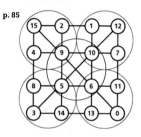

p. 86 After 3 days

We are indebted to a number of fellow puzzlers and thinkers who have provided us with inspiration for this book, in particular, Paul Sloane and also Dr. Edward de Bono, Boris A. Kordemsky, Victor Serebriakoff, Martin Gardner, Trevor Truran, Des MacHale & Dr. Diana Taylor.